CHILDCRAFT

THE HOW AND WHY LIBRARY

POEMS AND RHYMES

World Book, Inc.
a Scott Fetzer company
Chicago

World Book, Inc.
233 N. Michigan Avenue
Chicago, IL 60601 U.S.A.

Previous editions © 2004, 2003, 2000, 1996, 1995, 1994, 1993, 1991, 1990, 1989, 1987, 1986, 1985 World Book, Inc. © 1982, 1981, 1980, 1979, World Book-Childcraft International, Inc. © 1976, 1974, 1973, 1971, 1970, 1969, 1968, 1965, 1964 Field Enterprises Educational Corporation.

International Copyright © 2006, 2004, 2003, 2000, 1996, 1995, 1994, 1993, 1991, 1990, 1989, 1987, 1986, 1985 World Book, Inc. International Copyright © 1982, 1981, 1980, 1979 World Book-Childcraft International, Inc. International Copyright © 1976, 1974, 1973, 1971, 1970, 1969, 1968, 1965, 1964 Field Enterprises Educational Corporation.

ISBN 0-7166-5729-5 (set)
ISBN (Volume 1, Poems and Rhymes) 0-7166-5730-9

Printed in the United States of America
5 6 7 8 9 09 08 07 06 05

For information on other World Book publications, visit our Web site at **http://www.worldbook.com**

Acknowledgments

Aldis, Dorothy: "Ice", from *Everything and Anything* by Dorothy Aldis, copyright 1925-1927, renewed 1953, © 1954,1955 by Dorothy Aldis. "The Reason" from *All Together* by Dorothy Aldis, copyright 1925-1928, 1934, 1939, 1952, renewed 1953, © 1954-1956, 1962 by Dorothy Aldis, © 1967 by Roy E. Porter, renewed. Used by permission of G. P. Putnam's Sons, A Division of Penguin Young Readers Group, A Member of Penguin Group (USA) Inc., 345 Hudson Street, New York, NY 10014. All rights reserved.

Allen, Marie Louise: "Mitten Song" and "My Zipper Suit" from *A Pocketful Of Poems* by Marie Louise Allen. Text copyright © 1957 by Marie Allen Howart. Used by permission of HarperCollins Publishers.

Armour, Richard: "Good Sportsmanship" from *Night With Armour* by Richard Armour. By permission of the author.

Austin, Mary: "Grizzly Bear" from *The Children Sing In The Far West*. Copyright 1928 by Mary Austin, © renewed 1956 by Kenneth M. Chapman and Mary C. Wheelwright. Reprinted by permission of Houghton Mifflin Co. All rights reserved.

AvRutick, Alice Gilbert: "I Ate a Ton of Sugar" from *Poems From Sharon's Lunchbox* by Alice Gilbert, published by Delacorte Press, copyright © 1972 by Alice Gilbert. Reprinted by permission of the author.

Bacmeister, Rhoda W.: "Stars", from *Stories to Begin On* by Rhoda W. Bacmeister, illustrated by Tom Maley, copyright 1940 by E. P. Dutton, renewed © 1968 by Rhoda W. Bacmeister. Used by permission of Dutton Children's Books, A Division of Penguin Young Readers Group, A Member of Penguin Group (USA) Inc., 345 Hudson Street, New York, NY 10014. All rights reserved.

Baumann, G. W.: "The Night" from *Gold And Gods Of Peru*. By permission of Elisabeth Baumann.

Behn, Harry: Haiku: "In spring the chirping", "A mountain village", "How cool cut hay smells", "What a wonderful", and "When my canary" from *Cricket Songs,* Japanese haiku translated by Harry Behn. © 1964 Harry Behn. Copyright renewed 1992 Prescott Behn, Pamela Behn, Adam and Peter Behn. Used by permission of Marian Reiner.

Belloc, Hilaire: "The Elephant" from *Complete Verse* by Hilaire Belloc. (Copyright The Estate of Hilaire Belloc 1970) is reproduced by permission of PFD (www.pfd.co.uk) on behalf of the Estate of Hilaire Belloc.

Bernos de Gasztold, Carmen: "The Prayer of the Little Ducks" from *Prayers from the Ark* by Carmen Bernos de Gasztold, translated by Rumer Godden, copyright © 1962, renewed 1990 by Rumer Godden. Original Copyright 1947, © 1955 by Editions du Cloitre. Used by permission of Viking Penguin, A Division of Penguin Young Readers Group, A Member of Penguin Group (USA) Inc., 345 Hudson Street, New York, NY 10014. All rights reserved. Also reprinted by permission of Curtis Brown, Ltd.

Beyer, Evelyn: "Jump or Jiggle" and "The House of the Mouse" by Evelyn Beyer, from *Another Here and Now Story Book* by Lucy Sprague Mitchell, copyright 1937 by E. P. Dutton, renewed © 1965 by Lucy Sprague Mitchell. Used by permission of Dutton Children's Books, A Division of Penguin Young Readers Group, A Member of Penguin Group (USA) Inc., 345 Hudson Street, New York, NY 10014. All rights reserved.

Brooks, Gwendolyn: "Cynthia in the Snow" from *Bronzeville Boys And Girls*. Copyright © 1956 by Gwendolyn Brooks Blakely. Used by permission of HarperCollins Publishers.

Chute, Marchette: "My Teddy Bear" from *Rhymes About Us* by Marchette Chute. Published 1974 by E. P. Dutton. Reprinted by permission of Elizabeth Hauser.

Coatsworth, Elizabeth: "Who Is So Pretty?" from *Mouse Chorus* by Elizabeth Coatsworth, Genevieve Vaughn-Jackson illustrator, copyright © 1955 by Pantheon Books, Inc. Used by permission of Random House Children's Books, a division of Random House, Inc. "Bad Kittens" from *Compass Rose* by Elizabeth Coatsworth. Copyright 1929 by Coward-McCann, Inc., renewed © 1957 by Elizabeth Coatsworth. Used by permission of Coward-McCann, A Division of Penguin Young Readers Group, A Member of Penguin Group (USA) Inc., 345 Hudson Street, New York, NY 10014. All rights reserved.

De Forest, Charlotte: "A Lost Snowflake", "The Prancing Pony", and "The Song of the Frog" from *The Prancing Pony: Stories And Nursery Rhymes From Japan*. Copyright 1967 by John Weatherhill, Inc. Reprinted by permission of the publisher.

Eastwick, Ivy O.: "Moon-In-Water" by Ivy O. Eastwick. Courtesy of the author.

Consultant Committee

Contents

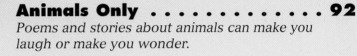
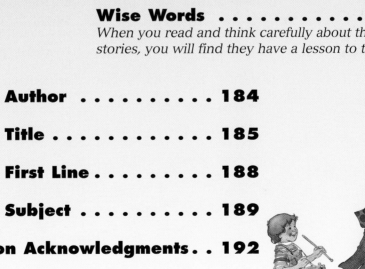

Introduction

Some words are so much fun that you just enjoy looking at and listening to them. Even a very young baby likes a bouncy rhythm and sounds that repeat. The pleasant patterns of sounds and words are what make poems and rhymes so much fun. And this book, *Poems and Rhymes,* is filled with them.

In the English language, Mother Goose rhymes are some of the best loved. You may already know some of them. If your family speaks another language, you may know some rhymes in that language, too. Some of the rhymes may be hundreds of years old, but they are so lively and bouncy, or so relaxing and soothing, that we still enjoy them today.

Did you know that rhymes and sayings also help you learn things? For example, the rhyme "One, two, buckle my shoe; three, four, shut the door" shows you in a fun way how to count. Poems and rhymes also express important ideas, such as doing your best, respecting people around you, and taking good care of yourself and your world.

Some of the poems in this book were written especially for you and other children about your age. These poems are about people and animals, night and day, and the world you know. You'll find some silly nonsense poems and rhymes, too. There are skipping rope rhymes, riddles, tongue twisters, and poems to say for fun. And there are some old stories with wise words. People have told them, listened to them, and learned from them for hundreds of years.

Try to read some of the poems and rhymes in this book every day (or ask a grown-up to read them to you). It will help you become a better reader and learn things more easily as you get older. And you'll have a good time!

This book has many features that will help you find your way through it.

Under some poems you will see a dictionary symbol: . After it, you will find a sentence that explains the meaning of a hard word from the poem.

This symbol tells you that a word's meaning is explained.

Each activity has a number. The higher the number, the more adult help you may need.

A **Try This!** activity has this colourful border.

This book also has activities that you can do at home. Look for the words **Try This!** over a coloured ball. The activity that follows is a way to learn more about poems and rhymes. For example, you can write special kinds of poems called haikus and cinquains, or you can create rhyming riddles. Take a moment to review the list of materials you will need and read the directions before you begin.

Turn to the **Index** to look up page numbers of subjects, titles, or authors that especially interest you.

If you enjoy learning about poems and rhymes, find out more about them in other resources, such as those listed below. Check them out at a bookstore or at the library in your school or town.

 **101 Fingerplays, Stories and Songs to use with Finger Puppets,** by Diane Briggs, 1998. *Young students will love these!*

Barney Rhymes with Mother Goose, Video (VHS), The Lyons Group, 1993, 30 minutes. *With song, dance, puzzles, and puppets, Barney and his friends help Mother Goose remember her favourite nursery rhymes.*

A Child's Treasury of Nursery Rhymes, Collected and illustrated by Kady MacDonald Denton, 1998. *In this book, more than 100 best-loved rhymes are illustrated in an amusing and delightful manner.*

January Rides the Wind, by Charlotte F. Otten, 1997. *A poem for each month, accompanied by beautiful illustrations, captures the feeling of the changing seasons.*

A Light in the Attic, by Shel Silverstein. *Many editions are available, the 20th anniversary edition, released in 2001, includes a recording of the author reciting poems from this book.*

The Random House Book of Poetry for Children, Collected by Jack Prelutsky, 2000. *Some 500 poems were selected by Prelutsky, himself a poet, and illustrated by Arnold Lobel, a Caldecott medalist and the creator of the Frog and Toad series.*

Riddle-Lightful: Oodles of Little Riddle Poems, by J. Patrick Lewis, 1998. *Can you guess the answers to these 32 riddle poems?*

Ring O' Roses, illustrated by L. Leslie Brooke, 1992. *A nursery-rhyme collection first published in 1922, this classic has been updated with new reproductions of Brooke's artwork.*

Sky Scrape/City Scape, selected by Jane Yolen, 1996. *This is a collection of poems about urban life, beautifully illustrated by Ken Condon.*

It's important to read—alone or with someone else—every day. In case you are wondering where to start, try picking poems about subjects you like, such as stars, frogs, or food. The subject index can help you find poems on different subjects. Below is a guide to help grown-ups decide what to read with you. It lists all the poems and stories in this book. The groupings show how well readers of different ages may like them or understand them.

LITERATURE TO READ TO PRE-READERS

For Fun

Poems and rhymes are
fun to hear and fun to say,
too. Poems have words that
sound pleasing. We enjoy
the ideas and feelings that
they give us. The words may
excite us or calm us down.
They may make us
laugh or feel sad.
Either way, they keep
our minds lively.

Higglety, Pigglety, Pop!

Mother Goose

Higglety, pigglety, pop!
The dog has eaten the mop;
  The pig's in a hurry,
  The cat's in a flurry,
Higglety, pigglety, pop!

Mary Had a Little Lamb

by Sara Josepha Hale

Mary had a little lamb,
  Its fleece was white as snow;
And everywhere that Mary went
  The lamb was sure to go.

It followed her to school one day,
  Which was against the rule;
It made the children laugh and play
  To see a lamb at school.

And so the teacher turned it out,
  But still it lingered near;
And waited patiently about
  Till Mary did appear.

"Why does the lamb love Mary so?"
  The eager children cry;
"Why, Mary loves the lamb, you know,"
  The teacher did reply.

Lingered means to go slowly, unwilling to leave.

I Love You, I Love You

author unknown

I love you, I love you,
I love you divine.
Please give me your bubble gum.
You're sitting on mine!

Question

author unknown

Do you love me
Or do you not?
You told me once
But I forgot.

15

Walking

by Grace Glaubitz

When Daddy
Walks
With Jean and me,
We have a
Lot of fun
'Cause we can't
Walk as fast
As he,
Unless we
Skip and
Run!
I stretch,
And stretch
My legs so far,
I nearly slip
And fall—
But how
Does Daddy
Take such steps?
He doesn't stretch
At all!

My Little Golden Sister

a Chinese nursery rhyme

My little golden sister
Rides a golden horse so slow;
She'll have to use a golden whip
To make her slow horse go.

A little golden fish
In a golden bowl has she;
And a golden bird is singing
On a golden cherry tree.

A smiling golden Buddha
In a golden temple stands,
With a tiny golden baby
In his gentle golden hands.

Two Little Sisters

a Chinese nursery rhyme

Two little sisters went walking one day,
Partly for exercise, partly for play.
They took with them kites which they wanted to fly,
One a big centipede, one a great butterfly.
Then up in a moment the kites floated high,
Like dragons that seemed to be touching the sky!

Georgie Porgie

Mother Goose

Georgie Porgie, pudding and pie,
Kissed the girls and made them cry;
When the boys came out to play,
Georgie Porgie ran away.

The House
That Jack Built

Mother Goose

This is the house that Jack built.

This is the malt
That lay in the house that Jack built.

This is the rat,
That ate the malt
That lay in the house that Jack built.

This is the cat,
That killed the rat,
That ate the malt
That lay in the house that Jack built.

This is the dog,
That worried the cat,
That killed the rat,
That ate the malt
That lay in the house that Jack built.

This is the cow with the crumpled horn,
That tossed the dog,
That worried the cat,
That killed the rat,
That ate the malt
That lay in the house that Jack built.

This is the maiden all forlorn,
That milked the cow with the crumpled horn,
That tossed the dog,
That worried the cat,
That killed the rat,
That ate the malt
That lay in the house that Jack built.

This is the man all tattered and torn,
That kissed the maiden all forlorn,

Malt means barley and grains.
Maiden all forlorn means
sad young lady.

That milked the cow with the crumpled horn,
That tossed the dog,
That worried the cat,
That killed the rat,
That ate the malt
That lay in the house that Jack built.

This is the priest all shaven and shorn,
That married the man all tattered and torn,
That kissed the maiden all forlorn,
That milked the cow with the crumpled horn,
That tossed the dog,
That worried the cat,
That killed the rat,
That ate the malt
That lay in the house that Jack built.

This is the cock that crowed in the morn,
That waked the priest all shaven and shorn,
That married the man all tattered and torn,
That kissed the maiden all forlorn,
That milked the cow with the crumpled horn,
That tossed the dog,
That worried the cat,
That killed the rat,
That ate the malt
That lay in the house that Jack built.

This is the farmer sowing his corn,
That kept the cock that crowed in the morn,
That waked the priest all shaven and shorn,
That married the man all tattered and torn,
That kissed the maiden all forlorn,
That milked the cow with the crumpled horn,
That tossed the dog,
That worried the cat,
That killed the rat,
That ate the malt
That lay in the house that Jack built.

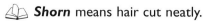 **Shorn** means hair cut neatly.

19

Old King Cole

Mother Goose

Old King Cole
Was a merry old soul,
And a merry old soul was he.
He called for his pipe,
And he called for his bowl,
And he called for his fiddlers three.

Every fiddler, he had a fiddle,
And a very fine fiddle had he,
Oh, there's none so rare
As can compare
With King Cole and his fiddlers three.

The Queen of Hearts

Mother Goose

The Queen of Hearts
She made some tarts,
All on a summer's day.
The Knave of Hearts
He stole the tarts,
And took them clean away.

The King of Hearts
Called for the tarts,
And beat the knave full sore,
The Knave of Hearts
Brought back the tarts,
And vowed he'd steal no more.

Knave of Hearts means Jack
of Hearts. *Knave* alone means
tricky, dishonest boy.
Vowed means promised.

Mary, Mary, Quite Contrary

Mother Goose

Mary, Mary, quite contrary,
   How does your garden grow?
With silver bells and cockleshells,
   And pretty maids all in a row.

Humpty Dumpty

Mother Goose

Humpty Dumpty sat on a wall,
Humpty Dumpty had a great fall.
   All the king's horses,
   And all the king's men,
Couldn't put Humpty together again.

Rub-a-Dub-Dub

Mother Goose

Rub-a-dub-dub,
Three men in a tub,
And who do you think they be?
The butcher, the baker,
The candlestick-maker;
Turn 'em out, knaves all three!

There Was an Old Woman

Mother Goose

There was an old woman
Lived under a hill,
And if she's not gone
She lives there still.

Barber, Barber

Mother Goose

Barber, barber, shave a pig,
How many hairs will make a wig?

Your Nose Is Running

by Jeff Moss

"Your nose is running," Mother said.
I answered, "Wow! That's really neat!"
"Why's that?" she asked. I said, "Because
I never knew my nose had feet."

Song of the Train

by David McCord

Clickety-clack,
Wheels on the track,
This is the way
They begin the attack:
Click-ety-clack,
Click-ety-clack,
Click-ety, *clack*-ety,
Click-ety
Clack.

Clickety-clack,
Over the crack,
Faster and faster
The song of the track:
Clickety-clack,
Clickety-clack,
Clickety, clackety,
Clackety,
Clack.

Riding in front,
Riding in back,
Everyone hears
The song of the track:
Clickety-clack,
Clickety-clack,
Clickety, *clickety,*
Clackety
Clack.

I Met a Man

author unknown

As I was going up the stair
I met a man who wasn't there.
He wasn't there again today—
Oh! how I wish he'd go away!

Ride a Cockhorse to Banbury Cross

Mother Goose

Ride a cockhorse to Banbury Cross,
To see a fine lady upon a white horse,
Rings on her fingers and bells on
   her toes,
And she shall have music wherever
   she goes.

Cockhorse means rocking horse.

24

There Was a Crooked Man

Mother Goose

There was a crooked man
    and he walked a crooked mile,
He found a crooked sixpence,
    against a crooked stile.
He bought a crooked cat,
    which caught a crooked mouse,
And they all lived together
    in a little crooked house.

Stile means step.
Sixpence was a British coin.

Peter, Peter, Pumpkin-Eater

Mother Goose

Peter, Peter, pumpkin-eater,
Had a wife and couldn't keep her.
He put her in a pumpkin shell,
And there he kept her very well.

Little Boy Blue

Mother Goose

Little Boy Blue, come blow your horn,
The sheep's in the meadow, the cow's in the corn;
But where is the boy who looks after the sheep?
He's under a haycock, fast asleep.
Will you wake him? No, not I,
For if I do, he's sure to cry.

📖 **Haycock** means small,
cone-shaped heap of hay.

Little Bo-Peep

Mother Goose

Little Bo-Peep has lost her sheep,
    And can't tell where to find them;
Leave them alone, and they'll come home,
    And bring their tails behind them.

Little Bo-Peep fell fast asleep,
    And dreamt she heard them bleating;
But when she awoke, she found it a joke,
    For they were still all fleeting.

Then up she took her little crook,
    Determined for to find them;
She found them indeed, but it made her heart bleed,
    For they'd left their tails behind them.

It happened one day, as Bo-Peep did stray
    Into a meadow hard by,
There she espied their tails side by side,
    All hung on a tree to dry.

She heaved a sigh, and wiped her eye,
    And over the hillocks went rambling,
And tried what she could, as a shepherdess should,
    To tack again each to its lambkin.

Bleating means making a sound like crying.
Fleeting means moving fast.

Crook means hooked stick.
Espied means saw.
Hillocks means small hills.

27

Little Miss Muffet

Mother Goose

Little Miss Muffet
Sat on a tuffet,
Eating her curds and whey;
There came a big spider,
Who sat down beside her
And frightened Miss Muffet away.

📖 **Tuffet** means a bunch of grass
or small mound.
Curds and whey means milky food,
like cottage cheese.

I Ate a Ton of Sugar

by Alice Gilbert

I ate a ton of sugar.
It made me very sweet.
It also made me very round—
now I can't find my feet.

Sing a Song of Sixpence

Mother Goose

Sing a song of sixpence,
    A pocket full of rye;
Four and twenty blackbirds
    Baked in a pie.

When the pie was opened,
    The birds began to sing;
Was not that a dainty dish
    To set before the king?

The king was in his counting-house,
    Counting out his money;
The queen was in the parlour,
    Eating bread and honey.

The maid was in the garden,
    Hanging out the clothes;
There came a little blackbird
    And snapped off her nose.
But there came a Jenny Wren
    And popped it on again.

📖 **Parlour** means living room.
Jenny Wren means female wren,
which is a type of small bird.

Little Tommy Tucker

Mother Goose

Little Tommy Tucker
Sings for his supper;
What shall we give him?
White bread and butter.

How shall he cut it
Without any knife?
How shall he marry
Without any wife?

Jack Sprat

Mother Goose

Jack Sprat could eat no fat,
His wife could eat no lean;
And so between them both,
   you see,
They licked the platter clean.

Simple Simon

Mother Goose

Simple Simon met a pieman
   Going to the fair;
Says Simple Simon to the pieman,
   "Let me taste your ware."

Says the pieman to Simple Simon,
   "Show me first your penny."
Says Simple Simon to the pieman,
   "Indeed, I have not any."

Simple Simon went a-fishing
   For to catch a whale;
But all the water he had got
   Was in his mother's pail.

He went to catch a dickybird,
   And thought he could not fail,
Because he had a pinch of salt
   To put upon its tail.

Ware means goods for sale.
Dickybird means small bird.

To Market, to Market

Mother Goose

To market, to market,
To buy a fat pig,
Home again, home again,
Jiggety-jig.

To market, to market,
To buy a fat hog,
Home again, home again,
Jiggety-jog.

To market, to market,
To buy a plum bun,
Home again, home again,
Market is done.

31

Hot Cross Buns

Mother Goose

Hot cross buns!
Hot cross buns!
One a penny, two a penny,
Hot cross buns!
If you have no daughters,
Give them to your sons.
One a penny, two a penny,
Hot cross buns!

If All the World Were Paper

Mother Goose

If all the world were paper,
And all the sea were ink,
And all the trees were bread and cheese,
What would we have to drink?

Little Jack Horner

Mother Goose

Little Jack Horner
Sat in the corner,
Eating a Christmas pie;
He put in his thumb,
And pulled out a plum,
And said, "What a good boy am I!"

Toot! Toot!

author unknown

A peanut sat on a railway track.
His heart was all aflutter.
The five-fifteen came rushing by—
Toot! Toot! Peanut butter!

Aflutter means beating fast.

I Eat My Peas
with Honey

author unknown

I eat my peas with honey;
I've done it all my life.
It makes the peas taste funny,
But it keeps them on the knife.

Pease Porridge Hot

Mother Goose

Pease porridge hot,
   Pease porridge cold,
Pease porridge in the pot
   Nine days old.

Some like it hot,
   Some like it cold,
Some like it in the pot
   Nine days old.

Pease means
   peas.

Old Mother Hubbard

Mother Goose

Old Mother Hubbard
Went to the cupboard,
To fetch her poor dog a bone,
But when she got there
The cupboard was bare,
And so the poor dog had none.

She went to the baker's
To buy him some bread,
But when she came back
The poor dog was dead.

She went to the undertaker's
To buy him a coffin,
But when she came back
The poor dog was laughing.

She took a clean dish
To get him some tripe,
But when she came back
He was smoking a pipe.

She went to the fruiterer's
To buy him some fruit,
But when she came back
He was playing the flute.

Tripe means part of an animal's body used for food.

She went to the tailor's
To buy him a coat,
But when she came back
He was riding a goat.

She went to the hatter's
To buy him a hat,
But when she came back
He was feeding the cat.

She went to the barber's
To buy him a wig,
But when she came back
He was dancing a jig.

She went to the cobbler's
To buy him some shoes,
But when she came back
He was reading the news.

The dame made a curtsy,
The dog made a bow.
The dame said, "Your servant."
The dog said, "Bow-wow."

Dame means woman.

35

Rain, Rain

Mother Goose

Rain, rain,
Go away,
Come again another day.

It's Raining, It's Pouring

Mother Goose

It's raining, it's pouring,
The old man is snoring.
He went to bed
And bumped his head
And couldn't get up in the
   morning.

Doctor Foster Went to Gloucester

Mother Goose

Doctor Foster went to Gloucester
In a shower of rain;
He stepped in a puddle,
Right up to his middle,
And never went there again.

It's Blowing, It's Snowing

a Dutch nursery rhyme

It's blowing, it's snowing,
Children are tumbling down.
So tie your cap beneath your chin,
And run and fetch the washing in.

A Lost Snowflake

a Japanese nursery rhyme

The snowflakes fell, the first this year.
I caught one on my sleeve—right here!
I thought that we would play all day.
But then it melted—right away!

Rain on the Green Grass

Mother Goose

Rain on the green grass,
Rain on the tree,
Rain on the housetop,
But not on me.

Snowy Morning

by *Lilian Moore*

Wake
gently this morning
to a different day.
Listen.
There is no bray
of buses,
no brake growls,
no siren howls and
no horns
blow.
There is only
the silence
of a city
hushed
by snow.

Bray means loud, harsh sound,
like a donkey makes.

My Zipper Suit

by *Marie Louise Allen*

My zipper suit is bunny-brown—
The top zips up, the legs zip down.
I wear it every day.
My daddy brought it out from town.
Zip it up, and zip it down,
And hurry out to play!

Thaw

by *Eunice Tietjens*

The snow is soft,
    and how it squashes!
"Galumph, galumph!"
    go my galoshes.

Cynthia in the Snow

by Gwendolyn Brooks

IT SUSHES.
It hushes
The loudness in the road.
It flitter-twitters,
And laughs away from me.
It laughs a lovely whiteness,
And whitely whirs away,
To be
Some otherwhere,
Still white as milk or shirts.
So beautiful it hurts.

The Mitten Song

by Marie Louise Allen

"Thumbs in the thumb-place,
Fingers all together!"
This is the song
We sing in mitten-weather.
When it is cold,
It doesn't matter whether
Mittens are wool,
Or made of finest leather.
This is the song
We sing in mitten-weather:
"Thumbs in the thumb-place,
Fingers all together!"

Rock-a-Bye Baby

Mother Goose

Rock-a-bye, baby,
   Thy cradle is green,
Father's a nobleman,
   Mother's a queen;
And Betty's a lady,
   And wears a gold ring;
And Johnny's a drummer,
   And drums for the king.

Nobleman means a person of high rank.

Moon-Come-Out

by Eleanor Farjeon

Moon-Come-Out
And Sun-Go-In,
Here's a soft blanket
To cuddle your chin.

Moon-Go-In
And Sun-Come-Out,
Throw off the blanket
And bustle about.

Star-Light, Star-Bright

Mother Goose

Star-light, star-bright,
First star I see tonight;
I wish I may, I wish I might,
Have the wish I wish tonight.

The Owl Hooted

a Yuma Indian song

The owl hooted,
Telling of the morning star.
He hooted again,
Announcing the dawn.

I See the Moon

Mother Goose

I see the moon,
    And the moon sees me;
God bless the moon,
    And God bless me.

Jeremiah Obediah

Mother Goose

Jeremiah Obediah puffs, puffs, puffs;
When he gets his messages, he snuffs, snuffs, snuffs;
When he goes to school by day, he roars, roars, roars;
And when he goes to bed at night, he snores, snores, snores.

Wee Willie Winkie

Mother Goose

Wee Willie Winkie
 Runs through the town,
Upstairs and downstairs
 In his nightgown,
Rapping at the window,
 Crying through the lock,
"Are the children in their beds,
 For now it's eight o'clock?"

Diddle, Diddle, Dumpling

Mother Goose

Diddle, diddle, dumpling, my son John,
Went to bed with his trousers on;
One shoe off, and one shoe on,
Diddle, diddle, dumpling, my son John.

Hush-a-Bye Baby

Mother Goose

Hush-a-bye, baby, on the tree top,
When the wind blows the cradle will rock;
When the bough breaks the cradle will fall,
Down will come baby, cradle and all.

Bough means branch.

Hush, Baby, My Doll

Mother Goose

Hush, baby, my doll, I pray you don't cry,
And I'll give you some bread and some milk by and by;
Or, perhaps, you like custard, or, maybe, a tart—
Then to either you're welcome, with all my whole heart.

The Star

by Jane Taylor

Twinkle, twinkle little star,
How I wonder what you are,
Up above the world so high,
Like a diamond in the sky.

When the blazing sun is set,
And the grass with dew is wet,
Then you show your little light,
Twinkle, twinkle all the night.

Dew means water drops that
appear during the night.

Stars

by Rhoda W. Bacmeister

Bright stars, light stars,
Shining-in-the-night stars,
Little twinkly, winkly stars,
Deep in the sky!

Yellow stars, red stars,
Shine-when-I'm-in-bed stars,
Oh how many blinky stars,
Far, far away!

44

Down with the Lambs

author unknown

Down with the lambs,
　Up with the lark,
Run to bed, children,
　Before it gets dark.

📖 **Lark** means songbird.

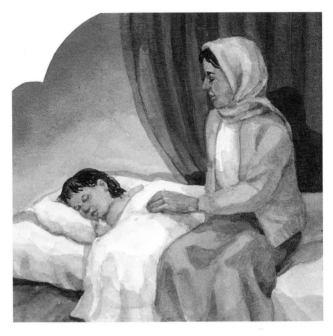

Hippity Hop to Bed

by Leroy F. Jackson

O it's hippity hop to bed!
I'd rather sit up instead.
But when father says "must,"
There's nothing but just
Go hippity hop to bed.

Early to Bed and Early to Rise

Mother Goose

The cock crows in the morn
To tell us to rise,
And he that lies late
Will never be wise:
For early to bed,
And early to rise,
Is the way to be healthy
And wealthy and wise.

Lullaby

an African Baka "Pygmy" poem

Sleep, sleep, little one;
Close your eyes, sleep, little one!
The night comes down, the hour has come,
Tomorrow it will be day.
Sleep, sleep, little one!
On your closed eyes day has fled.

You are warm. You have drunk,
Sleep, sleep, little one!
Sleep, tomorrow you will be big, you will be strong.
Sleep, tomorrow you will take the bow and the knife.

Sleep, you will be strong,
You will be straight, and I bent.
Sleep, tomorrow it is you,
but it is mother always.

Away in the East

a North American Zuni poem

Away in the east,
the rain clouds care for
the little corn plants
as a mother cares for
her baby.

Now I Lay Me Down to Sleep

author unknown

Now I lay me down to sleep,
I pray the Lord my soul to keep;
And if I die before I wake,
I pray the Lord my soul to take.

A Bedtime Prayer

author unknown

Matthew, Mark, Luke, and John,
Bless the bed that I lie on.
    Four corners to my bed,
    Four angels round my head;
    One to watch and one to pray
    And two to bear my soul away.

Willow Leaves Murmur

a Chinese nursery rhyme

Willow leaves murmur, hua-la-la.
Sleep, precious baby, close to mama.
Hua-la-la, baby, smile in your sleep;
You'll have only sweet dreams
While my watch I keep.

Go to Sleep

a French nursery rhyme

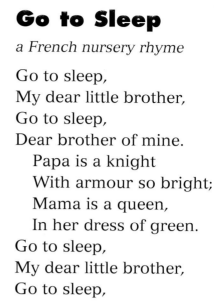

Go to sleep,
My dear little brother,
Go to sleep,
Dear brother of mine.
  Papa is a knight
  With armour so bright;
  Mama is a queen,
  In her dress of green.
Go to sleep,
My dear little brother,
Go to sleep,
Dear brother of mine.

Armour means a metal suit that protects a person in battle.

48

Lullaby

by Christina Rossetti

Lullaby, oh, lullaby!
Flowers are closed and lambs are sleeping;
Lullaby, oh, lullaby!
Stars are up, the moon is peeping;
Lullaby, oh, lullaby!
While the birds are silence keeping;
Lullaby, oh, lullaby!
Sleep, my baby, fall a-sleeping,
Lullaby, oh, lullaby!

Lullaby to a Naughty Baby

a Venezuelan nursery rhyme

Lullaby, naughty child,
Your nonsense drives your mother wild.

Lullaby, arrurru,
What can Mama do with you?

Work all day, up all night,
By morning nothing's going right.

Lullaby, arrurru,
What can Mama do with you?

The Song of the Frog

a Japanese nursery rhyme

So hushaby, baby, if you'll go to sleep,
I'll give you a pretty red flower to keep.
But if you keep crying, a big ugly frog
Will croak by your side—*kerchog! kerchog!*

The Night

an African Fipa poem

The night is over
before one has finished counting the stars.

Night

by Lois Weakley McKay

My kitten walks on velvet feet
And makes no sound at all;
And in the doorway nightly sits
To watch the darkness fall.

I think he loves the lady, Night,
And feels akin to her
Whose footsteps are as still as his,
Whose touch as soft as fur.

📖 **Feels akin to her** means to feel like
    her or related to her.

Good Night

by Rose Fyleman

The rabbits play no more,
   The little birds are weary,
The buttercups are folded up—
   Good night, good night, my dearie.

The children in the country,
   The children in the city,
Go to their beds with nodding heads—
   Good night, good night, my pretty.

City

by Langston Hughes

In the morning the city
Spreads its wings
Making a song
In stone that sings.

In the evening the city
Goes to bed
Hanging lights
About its head.

The Water Bug

a Yuma Indian poem

The water bug
is drawing the shadows of evening
toward him across the water.

Things to Know

Rhymes can make it easy and fun to remember all kinds of things, such as letters of the alphabet, days of the week, and seasons in a year. Rhymes can also help us see and think about all kinds of new things. Would you believe they can even make learning manners fun? Try these rhymes and see how many things they help you learn and remember.

An Animal Alphabet

Mother Goose

A is for ant.
Where there's one, there are many.
You either see lots
or you don't see any.

B is for bear
asleep in its den.
When spring comes around
it will wake up again.

Cc

C is for cat,
so soft and so furry,
dainty and curious,
mewy and purry.

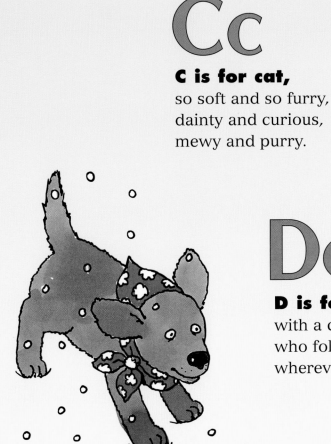

Dd

D is for dog
with a cold wet nose,
who follows its master
wherever he goes.

Ee

E is for eagle
that soars through the air
and hunts from the sky
when the weather is fair.

Ff

F is for fly

that makes a loud buzz
whenever it flies—
which it often does.

Gg

G is for goat

on a mountain high,
grazing on grass
while the clouds roll by.

Grazing means munching
or feeding.

Hh

H is for horse,

whose feet go clup-clup.
It can run like the wind,
and it sleeps standing up.

56

Ii

I is for iguana.

A dragon it's not.
It's a sun-loving lizard
that lives where it's hot.

Jj

J is for jay,

a bird far from quiet.
Three jays in a tree
are a fine-feathered riot!

Kk

K is for koala.

It looks like a bear,
but it eats eucalyptus,
and bears wouldn't dare.

Ll

L is for lion,
who lies in the sun
and never eats lunch
on a hamburger bun.

Mm

M is for mouse,
a tiny, shy beast
that is clever at finding
its way to a feast.

Nn

N is for narwhal
that swims all about—
a small kind of whale
with a horn on its snout.

Oo

O is for otter,
who often eats
(without any lemon)
fishy treats.

Pp

P is for penguin,
a bird that won't freeze
when it swims like a fish
in icy-cold seas.

Qq

Q is for quail,
who is hard to see
when standing in dry leaves,
quietly.

Rr

R is for robin
with a cheery red breast,
who lays her new eggs
in a shaggy brown nest.

Ss

S is for snail
with its house on its back,
who slides slowly along
on a slippery track.

Tt

T is for toad
and also for treat.
A treat for a toad
is a bug to eat!

Uu

U is for unicorn,
a fairy-tale horse
with a horn on its head.
That's magic, of course!

Vv

V is for vulture

that feeds on things dead.
(It would probably rather
eat pancakes instead!)

Ww

W is for worm

that eats earth for dinner.
If that's what we ate,
we'd all be much thinner!

Xx

X as in fox

that hunts in the night
and can hear any noise,
no matter how slight.

Yy

Y is for yak
with its shaggy, thick hair.
It lives high in the mountains,
and it's c-cold up there!

Zz

Z is for zebra
It's black, striped with white—
or else white with black stripes—
I'm not sure which is right.

One for the Money

Mother Goose

One for the money,
And two for the show,
Three to get ready,
And four to go.

One for Anger

Mother Goose

One for anger,
Two for mirth,
Three for a wedding,
Four for a birth,
Five for rich,
Six for poor,
Seven for a witch,
I can tell you no more.

 Mirth means fun and
laughter.

1, 2, 3, 4, 5!

Mother Goose

1, 2, 3, 4, 5!
Once I caught a fish alive;
6, 7, 8, 9, 10!
Then I let it go again.

1, 2, 3, 4

Mother Goose

1, 2, 3, 4,
Mary at the cottage door;
5, 6, 7, 8,
Eating cherries off a plate.

64

Seven Blackbirds in a Tree

Mother Goose

Seven blackbirds in a tree,
Count them and see what they be.
One for sorrow
Two for joy
Three for a girl
Four for a boy
Five for silver
Six for gold
Seven for a secret
That's never been told.

One, Two, Buckle My Shoe

Mother Goose

One, two,
Buckle my shoe;

Three, four,
Knock at the door;

Five, six,
 Pick up sticks;

Seven, eight,
 Lay them straight;

Nine, ten,
 A big fat hen.

The End

by A. A. Milne
illustrated by E. H. Shepard

When I was One,
I had just begun.

When I was Two,
I was nearly new.

When I was Three,
I was hardly Me.

When I was Four,
I was not much more.

When I was Five,
I was just alive.

But now I am Six,
  I'm clever as clever.
So I think I'll be six now
  for ever and ever.

This Old Man

author unknown

This old man, he played one,
He played knick-knack on my drum.
Knick-knack, paddy-whack,
Give a dog a bone,
This old man came rolling home.

2

This old man, he played two,
He played knick-knack on my shoe.
Knick-knack, paddy-whack,
Give a dog a bone,
This old man came rolling home.

This old man, he played three,
He played knick-knack on my knee.
Knick-knack, paddy-whack,
Give a dog a bone,
This old man came rolling home.

3

This old man, he played four,
He played knick-knack on my door.
Knick-knack, paddy-whack,
Give a dog a bone,
This old man came rolling home.

This old man, he played five,
He played knick-knack on my hive.
Knick-knack, paddy-whack,
Give a dog a bone,
This old man came rolling home.

This old man, he played six,
He played knick-knack with some sticks.
Knick-knack, paddy-whack,
Give a dog a bone,
This old man came rolling home.

This old man, he played seven,
He played knick-knack up to heaven.
Knick-knack, paddy-whack,
Give a dog a bone,
This old man came rolling home.

This old man, he played eight,
He played knick-knack on my gate.
Knick-knack, paddy-whack,
Give a dog a bone,
This old man came rolling home.

This old man, he played nine,
He played knick-knack on my vine.
Knick-knack, paddy-whack,
Give a dog a bone,
This old man came rolling home.

10

This old man, he played ten,
He played knick-knack once again.
Knick-knack, paddy-whack,
Give a dog a bone,
This old man came rolling home.

What Is Pink?

by Christina Rossetti

What is pink? a rose is pink
By the fountain's brink.
What is red? a poppy's red
In its barley bed.
What is blue? the sky is blue
Where the clouds float thro'.
What is white? a swan is white
Sailing in the light.
What is yellow? pears are yellow,
Rich and ripe and mellow.
What is green? the grass is green,
With small flowers between.
What is violet? clouds are violet
In the summer twilight.
What is orange? why, an orange,
Just an orange!

Roses are Red

author unknown

Roses are red
Violets are blue
Daisies are yellow
Sunflowers are too.

The Purple Cow
by Gelett Burgess

I never saw a Purple Cow,
I never hope to see one,
But I can tell you, anyhow,
I'd rather see than be one!

Yellow
by David McCord

Green is go,
and red is stop,
and yellow is peaches
with cream on top.

Earth is brown,
and blue is sky;
yellow looks well
on a butterfly.

Clouds are white,
black, pink, or mocha;
yellow's a dish of
tapioca.

Wash on Monday

Mother Goose

Wash on Monday,
Iron on Tuesday,
Mend on Wednesday,
Churn on Thursday,
Clean on Friday,
Bake on Saturday,
Rest on Sunday.

Mend means repair or
  fix something.
Churn means make butter.

Solomon Grundy

Mother Goose

Solomon Grundy,
Born on a Monday,
Christened on a Tuesday,
Married on a Wednesday,
Took ill on a Thursday,
Worse on Friday,
Died on Saturday,
Buried on Sunday.
This is the end
of Solomon Grundy.

Christened means baptized.
  A Christening or baptism
  is a Christian ceremony.

Monday's Child

Mother Goose

Monday's child is fair of face,
Tuesday's child is full of grace,
Wednesday's child is full of woe,
Thursday's child has far to go,
Friday's child is loving and giving,
Saturday's child works hard for his living,
And the child that is born on the Sabbath day
Is bonny and blithe and good and gay.

Fair of face means beautiful.
Grace means charming ways or manners.
Woe means sadness or sorrow.
Sabbath day means Sunday, the Christian day of rest.
Bonny and blithe means pretty and cheerful.

Make a Poem with a Shape

Some poems are like pictures with words. But you can make a poem that is really a picture. These picture-poems are meant to be read and to be looked at, too.

You Will Need:

paper
a pencil or felt-tipped pen

EARS
NOSE EYES FAITHFUL FRIEND WAG
BARK BONE BOW FLEAS TAIL
WOW SNIFF SPOT
CURLY HUNGRY HAPPY WARM
CUTE WOOF
PAW WOOF

What To Do:

1. Pick a thing you would like to write about. It can be a plant or animal, something you see outdoors, your house, or even a toy or bus.

Here are some idea starters for poems with a shape. Think of some other ideas to try.

sun	tree	dog
bicycle	cloud	rocket
telephone	horse	ice cream cone

2. Write down some words for parts of the thing. Write down words that describe it, too. Try to think of words that tell exactly how it looks, sounds, feels, smells, or tastes.

3. On another sheet of paper, draw the shape of the thing. Now you are ready to make your poem.

4. Pick words from your list for each part of the shape and write them where they belong. You can repeat words as often as you need to.

5. Instead of drawing a shape with lines, try using the words themselves to make a poem with a shape. Do you see the poem that is shaped like an eye?

BRIGHT
SHINE ORANGE FIRE HOT SHINE
BRIGHT ORANGE SUN ORANGE BRIGHT
SHINE HOT FIRE ORANGE BRIGHT
BRIGHT

I CAN SEE YOU!
I SEE WHEN YOU THINK I DON'T.
I WATCH THE SILLY THINGS YOU DO.
DOING. I SEE WHAT YOU ARE
I CAN SEE YOU!

Hickory, Dickory, Dock

Mother Goose

Hickory, dickory, dock,
The mouse ran up the clock.
    The clock struck one,
    The mouse ran down,
Hickory, dickory, dock.

A Diller, a Dollar

Mother Goose

A diller, a dollar,
A ten o'clock scholar!
What makes you come so soon?
You used to come at ten o'clock,
But now you come at noon.

Scholar means student.

The Clock

Mother Goose

Tick, tock, tick, tock,
Merrily sings the clock;
    It's time for work,
    It's time for play,
So it sings throughout the day.
Tick, tock, tick, tock,
Merrily sings the clock.

Bell Horses

Mother Goose

Bell horses, bell horses,
    What time of day?
One o'clock, two o'clock,
    Three and away.

Spring Is Showery, Flowery, Bowery

author unknown

Spring is showery,
flowery, bowery;

Summer: hoppy,
croppy, poppy;

Autumn: slippy,
drippy, nippy;

Winter: breezy,
sneezy, freezy.

Ice

by Dorothy Aldis

When it is the winter time
   I run up the street
And I make the ice laugh
   With my little feet—
"Crickle, crackle, crickle
   Crrreeet, crrreeet, crrreeet."

Daylight Saving Time

by Phyllis McGinley

In Spring when maple buds are red,
We turn the Clock an hour ahead;
Which means, each April that arrives,
We lose an hour
Out of our lives.

Who cares? When Autumn birds in flocks
Fly southward, back we turn the Clocks,
And so regain a lovely thing—
That missing hour
We lost last spring.

📖 **Daylight Saving Time** is the time that is one
    hour ahead of standard time. In some parts of
    the world, people turn their clocks ahead one
    hour in the spring and back one hour in the
    autumn to allow for an extra hour of daylight after
    working hours. This is a rhyme about that custom.

Our Children's Earth

an African nomadic pastoralists verse

Treat the earth well,
It was not given to us by our fathers,
But is lent to us by our children.

Enjoy the Earth

an African Yoruba verse

Enjoy the earth gently
Enjoy the earth gently
For if the earth is spoiled
It cannot be repaired
Enjoy the earth gently.

Spoiled means injured or destroyed.

Happy Thought

by Robert Louis Stevenson

The world is so full of a
    number of things,
I'm sure we should all be as
    happy as kings.

Moon-in-Water

by Ivy O. Eastwick

Three Wise Men of Gotham
thought the Moon was cheese
and tried to fish it out
of the river—if you please!
but all the little tadpoles
trilled a little tune:
"You'll never, never catch it—
it's the Moon!
　　　　Moon!
　　　　　　MOON!"

By the Sandy Water

a Papago Indian verse

By the sandy water I breathe in the odour of the sea;
From there the wind comes and blows over the world.
By the sandy water I breathe in the odour of the sea;
From there the clouds come and rain falls over the world.

If Once You Have
Slept on an Island

by Rachel Field

If once you have slept on an island
   You'll never be quite the same;
You may look as you looked the day before
   And go by the same old name,

You may bustle about in street and shop;
   You may sit at home and sew,
But you'll see blue water and wheeling gulls
   Wherever your feet may go.

You may chat with the neighbours of this and that
   And close to your fire keep,
But you'll hear ship whistle and lighthouse bell
   And tides beat through your sleep.

Oh, you won't know why, and you can't say how
   Such change upon you came,
But—once you have slept on an island
   You'll never be quite the same!

Bustle means hurry.
Tides means the rise and fall of the ocean about every 12 hours.

This Land

a South American Akawaio verse

This land is where we belong
This land is where we are at home, we know its ways
This land is needed for those who come after
We know where to find all this land provides for us
This land keeps us together within its mountains.

Ayii, Ayii

an Eastern Inuit verse

Ayii, Ayii,
The great sea has set me in motion,
Set me adrift,
And I move as a weed in the river.
The arch of the sky
And mightiness of storms
Encompasses me,
And I am left
Trembling with joy.

Encompasses means surrounds.

When Jacky's a Good Boy

author unknown

When Jacky's a good boy,
   He shall have cakes and custard;
But when he does nothing but cry,
   He shall have nothing but mustard.

Table Manners

by Gelett Burgess

The Goops they lick their fingers,
   And the Goops they lick their knives;
They spill their broth on the tablecloth—
   Oh, they lead disgusting lives!
The Goops they talk while eating,
   And loud and fast they chew;
And that is why I'm glad that I
   Am not a Goop—are you?

Patience

author unknown

Patience is a virtue,
   Virtue is a grace;
Both put together
   Make a very pretty face.

📖 **Virtue** means goodness.

Whatever You Do

author unknown

One, two, whatever you do,
Start it well and carry it through.
Try, try, never say die,
Things will come right,
   you know, by and by.

Good Sportsmanship

by Richard Armour

Good sportsmanship we hail, we sing,
   It's always pleasant when you spot it.
There's only one unhappy thing:
   You have to lose to prove you've got it.

Good, Better, Best

author unknown

Good, better, best.
Never rest
'Til good be better
And better, best.

One Thing at a Time

author unknown

One thing at a time
   And that done well,
Is a very good rule,
   As many can tell.

Say Well and Do Well

author unknown

Say well and do well
End with one letter;
Say well is good,
Do well is better.

Thingumajigs

by Irene Keller
illustrated by Dick Keller

Thingumajigs
Eat toads and snails.
And pick their teeth
With their fingernails.

I brush
after
meals!

They slurp their soup,
They rock their chairs,
And they eat their dinner
In their underwear.

My table manners are the best you'll
ever see. It's always such a pleasure
when you eat with me.

Thingumajigs sulk
And Thingumajigs say,
"If I won't win
Then I won't play."

Good sports do the best they can.
We can do the same.
We win some and we lose some,
but we're always in the game.

They don't clean up
And they don't do chores,
But they're very good
At slamming doors.

Help
out!

Do your
share!
Pitch
in!

Play
fair!

Animals Only

Animals can make you laugh or make you wonder. So can poems and stories about them. Turn the pages to see for yourself!

Froggie, Froggie

a Chinese nursery rhyme

Froggie, froggie,
Hoppity-hop!
When you get to the sea
You do not stop.

Plop!

The Prancing Pony

a Japanese nursery rhyme

Your prancing, dancing pony—
    Oh, please don't tie him here.
This cherry tree's in blossom—
    Oh, dear, dear, dear!

He'll prance and dance and whinny,
    He'll neigh and stamp and call,
And down the soft, pink blossoms
    Will fall, fall, fall!

94

Donkey, Donkey

Mother Goose

Donkey, donkey, old and grey,
Open your mouth and gently bray;
Lift your ears and blow your horn,
To wake the world this sleepy morn.

Mary Had a Pretty Bird

Mother Goose

Mary had a pretty bird,
Feathers bright and yellow,
Slender legs, upon my word,
He was a pretty fellow.

The sweetest notes he always sang,
Which much delighted Mary;
And near the cage she'd ever sit
To hear her own canary.

Three Little Kittens

Mother Goose

Three little kittens
They lost their mittens,
And they began to cry,
"Oh, mother dear,
We sadly fear
Our mittens we have lost."

"What? lost your mittens,
You naughty kittens!
Then you shall have no pie."
"Mee-ow, mee-ow, mee-ow."
"No, you shall have no pie."

The three little kittens
They found their mittens,
And they began to cry,
"Oh, mother dear,
See here, see here,
Our mittens we have found!"

"Put on your mittens,
You silly kittens,
And you shall have some pie."
"Purr-r, purr-r, purr-r,
Oh, let us have some pie."

The three little kittens
Put on their mittens,
And soon ate up the pie.
"Oh, mother dear,
We greatly fear
Our mittens we have soiled."

"What? soiled your mittens,
You naughty kittens!"
Then they began to sigh,
"Mee-ow, mee-ow, mee-ow."
Then they began to sigh.

The three little kittens
They washed their mittens,
And hung them out to dry;
"Oh, mother dear,
See here, see here,
Our mittens we have washed."

"What! washed your mittens,
Then you're good kittens,
But I smell a rat close by."
"Mee-ow, mee-ow, mee-ow.
We smell a rat close by."

Soiled means made dirty.

97

I Saw a Ship

Mother Goose

I saw a ship a-sailing,
A-sailing on the sea.
And, oh, it was all laden
With pretty things for thee.

There were comfits in the cabin,
And apples in the hold,
The sails were made of silk,
And the masts of beaten gold.

The four and twenty sailors
That stood between the decks,
Were four and twenty white mice
With chains about their necks.

The captain was a duck,
With a packet on his back,
And when the ship began to move
The captain said, "Quack, quack!"

Laden means loaded or filled.
Thee means you.
Comfits means sweets.
Hold means lower deck.

Three Blind Mice

Mother Goose

Three blind mice, see how they run!
They all ran after the farmer's wife,
Who cut off their tails with a carving knife,
Did you ever see such a thing in your life,
    As three blind mice?

Pussycat, Pussycat

Mother Goose

Pussycat, pussycat, where have you been?
I've been to London to visit the Queen.
Pussycat, pussycat, what did you there?
I frightened a little mouse under her chair.

There Once Was a Fish

Mother Goose

There once was a fish.
(What more could you wish?)

He lived in the sea.
(Where else would he be?)

He was caught on a line.
(Whose line if not mine?)

So I brought him to you.
(What else should I do?)

Bow, Wow, Wow

author unknown

Bow, wow, wow,
Whose dog art thou?
Little Tom Tinker's dog,
Bow, wow, wow.

📖 **Art thou** means are you.

Fuzzy Wuzzy

author unknown

Fuzzy Wuzzy was a bear,
Fuzzy Wuzzy had no hair.
Fuzzy Wuzzy wasn't fuzzy,
Was he?

Oh Where Has My Little Dog Gone?

Mother Goose

Oh where, oh where has my little
  dog gone?
  Oh where, oh where can he be?
With his ears cut short and his tail
  cut long,
  Oh where, oh where is he?

Hoddley, Poddley

Mother Goose

Hoddley, poddley, puddles and fogs,
Cats are to marry poodle dogs;
Cats in blue jackets and dogs in red hats,
What will become of the mice and the rats?

📖 **Fogs** means clouds or mist.

Two Cats of Kilkenny

Mother Goose

There once were two cats of Kilkenny,
Each thought there was one cat too many;
So they fought and they fit,
And they scratched and they bit,
Till, excepting their nails
And the tips of their tails,
Instead of two cats, there weren't any.

The Elephant Trunk

author unknown

The elephant carries a great
  big trunk;
He never packs it with clothes;
It has no lock and it has no key,
But he takes it wherever
  he goes.

Where Bananas Grow

author unknown

Way down South, where bananas grow,
A grasshopper stepped on an elephant's toe.
The elephant cried with tears in his eyes,
"Why don't you pick on someone your own size?"

Whisky Frisky

author unknown

Whisky Frisky,
Hippity-hop
Up he goes
To the treetop!

Whirly, twirly
Round and round,
Down he scampers
To the ground.

Furly, curly,
What a tail!
Tall as a feather,
Broad as a sail!

Where's his supper?
In the shell,
Snap, cracky,
Out it fell.

I Had a Little Hobby Horse

Mother Goose

I had a little hobby horse,
And it was dapple grey;
Its head was made of pea-straw,
Its tail was made of hay.

A Wee Little Worm

by James Whitcomb Riley

A wee little worm in a hickory-nut
 Sang, happy as he could be,
"O I live in the heart of the whole round world,
 And it all belongs to me!"

Hey, Diddle, Diddle

Mother Goose

Hey, diddle, diddle!
 The cat and the fiddle,
The cow jumped over the moon;
 The little dog laughed
 To see such sport,
And the dish ran away with the spoon.

Hickety, Pickety, My Black Hen

Mother Goose

Hickety, pickety, my black hen,
She lays eggs for gentlemen;
Gentlemen come every day
To see what my black hen doth lay.
Sometimes nine and sometimes ten,
Hickety, pickety, my black hen.

Doth means does.

Baa, Baa Black Sheep

Mother Goose

Baa, Baa, black sheep,
Have you any wool?
Yes sir, yes sir,
Three bags full;

One for my master,
And one for my dame,
And one for the little boy
Who lives down the lane.

My Teddy Bear

by Marchette Chute

A teddy bear is a faithful friend.
You can pick him up at either end.
His fur is the colour of breakfast toast,
And he's always there when you need him most.

Nature Note

by Arthur Guiterman

Undoubtedly the Kangaroos
   Have fun;
They hop because they do not choose
   To run.

The Rabbit

by Elizabeth Madox Roberts

When they said the time to hide was mine,
I hid back under a thick grapevine.

And while I was still for the time to pass,
A little grey thing came out of the grass.

He hopped his way through the melon bed
And sat down close by a cabbage head.

He sat down close where I could see,
And his big still eyes looked hard at me,

His big eyes bursting out of the rim,
And I looked back very hard at him.

Holding Hands

by Lenore M. Link

Elephants walking
Along the trails

Are holding hands
By holding tails.

Trunks and tails
Are handy things

When elephants walk
In circus rings.

Elephants work
And elephants play

And elephants walk
And feel so gay.

And when they walk—
It never fails

They're holding hands
By holding tails.

The Elephant

by Hilaire Belloc

When people call this beast to mind,
They marvel more and more
At such a *little* tail behind,
So LARGE a trunk before.

Once I Saw a Little Bird

author unknown

Once I saw a little bird
   Come hop, hop, hop,
I cried, "Little bird,
   Will you stop, stop, stop?"

I was going to the window
   To say, "How do you do?"
But he shook his little tail
   And away he flew.

The Lizard

by John Gardner

The Lizard is a timid thing
That cannot dance or fly or sing;
He hunts for bugs beneath the floor
And longs to be a dinosaur.

Timid means shy.

The Hummingbird

by Jack Prelutsky

The ruby-throated hummingbird
is hardly bigger than this WORD.

The Wise Old Owl

author unknown

A wise old owl lived in an oak;
The more he saw the less he spoke;
The less he spoke the more he heard.
Why can't we all be like that wise old bird?

Little Robin Redbreast

Mother Goose

Little Robin Redbreast sat upon a tree,
Up went Pussycat, and down went he;
Down came Pussy, and away Robin ran;
Said little Robin Redbreast, "Catch me if you can."

Little Robin Redbreast jumped upon a wall,
Pussycat jumped after him, and almost got a fall;
Little Robin chirped and sang, and what did Pussy say?
Pussycat said, "Mew," and Robin jumped away.

Grizzly Bear

by Mary Austin

If you ever, ever, ever meet a grizzly bear,
You must never, never, never ask him *where*
He is going,
Or *what* he is doing;
For if you ever, ever dare
To stop a grizzly bear,
You will never meet *another* grizzly bear.

I Had a Little Pig

author unknown

I had a little pig,
I fed him in a trough,
He got so fat
His tail dropped off.
So I got me a nail,
And I made my little pig
A brand new tail.

Three Young Rats

author unknown

Three young rats with black felt hats,
Three young ducks with white straw flats,
Three young dogs with curling tails,
Three young cats with demiveils,
Went out to walk with two young pigs,
In satin vests and sorrel wigs,
But suddenly it changed to rain,
And so they all went home again.

Demiveils means short veils.
Sorrel means light reddish-brown.

Who Is So Pretty?

by Elizabeth Coatsworth

Skitter, skatter,
Leap and squeak!
We've been dancing
Half the week.

Under the sofa,
Along the shelf,
Every mouse
Is wild as an elf.

Big round ear
And bright black eye,
Nimble and natty,
Limber and spry—

Who is so pretty,
Who is so neat,
As a little mouse dancing
On little grey feet?

📖 **Nimble** means quick.
Natty means trim.
Limber means moving easily.
Spry means active.

Mice

by Rose Fyleman

I think mice
Are rather nice.

Their tails are long,
Their faces small,
They haven't any
Chins at all.
Their ears are pink,
Their teeth are white,
They run about
The house at night.
They nibble things
They shouldn't touch
And no one seems
To like them much.

But *I* think mice
Are nice.

Jump or Jiggle

by Evelyn Beyer

Frogs jump
Caterpillars hump

Worms wiggle
Bugs jiggle

Rabbits hop
Horses clop

Snakes slide
Sea gulls glide

Mice creep
Deer leap

Puppies bounce
Kittens pounce

Lions stalk—
But—
I walk!

The House of the Mouse

by Lucy Sprague Mitchell

The house of the mouse
is a wee little house,
a green little house in the grass,
which big clumsy folk
may hunt and may poke
and still never see as they pass
this sweet little, neat little,
wee little, green little,
cuddle-down hide-away
house in the grass.

The City Mouse and the Garden Mouse

by Christina Rossetti

The city mouse lives in a house;
The garden mouse lives in a bower,
He's friendly with the frogs and toads,
And sees the pretty plants in flower.

The city mouse eats bread and cheese.
The garden mouse eats what he can;
We will not grudge him seeds and stalks,
Poor little timid furry man.

Bower means a shelter made of tree branches
and vines.

Bees

by Jack Prelutsky

Every bee
that
ever was
was
partly
sting
and partly
. . . buzz.

Mouse

by Hilda Conkling

Little Mouse in grey velvet,
Have you had a cheese-breakfast?
There are no crumbs on your coat,
Did you use a napkin?
I wonder what you had to eat,
And who dresses you in grey velvet?

A Kitten

by Eleanor Farjeon

He's nothing much but fur
And two round eyes of blue,
He has a giant purr
And a midget mew.

He darts and pats the air,
He starts and cocks his ear,
When there is nothing there
For him to see and hear.

He runs around in rings,
But why we cannot tell;
With sideways leaps he springs
At things invisible—

Then halfway through a leap
His startled eyeballs close,
And he drops off to sleep
With one paw on his nose.

The Bad Kittens

by Elizabeth Coatsworth

You may call, you may call,
But the little black cats won't hear you,
The little black cats are maddened
By the bright green light of the moon,
They are whirling and running and hiding,
They are wild who were once so confiding,
They are crazed when the moon is riding—
You will not catch the kittens soon.
They care not for saucers of milk,
They think not of pillows of silk,
Your softest, crooningest call
Is less than the buzzing of flies.
They are seeing more than you see,
They are hearing more than you hear,
And out of the darkness they peer
With a goblin light in their eyes.

Confiding means trusting.
Crooningest means most musical.

119

The Fox Went Out on a Chilly Night

a folk song

The fox went out on a chilly night,
And begged the moon to give him light,
For he had many a mile to go that night
Before he reached the town-o!
    Town-o! town-o!
For he had many a mile to go that night
Before he reached the town-o!

Well he ran 'til he came to a great big pen,
Where the ducks and the geese were kept therein.
"A couple of you gonna grease my chin
Before I leave this town-o!
  Town-o! town-o!
A couple of you gonna grease my chin
Before I leave this town-o!"

He grabbed the grey goose by the neck,
And flung a duck across his back;
He did not mind the "Quack! quack! quack!"
And their legs all dangling down-o!
   Down-o! down-o!
He did not mind the "Quack! quack! quack!"
And their legs all dangling down-o!

Old Mother Flipper Flapper jumped out of bed,
Out of the window she popped her head,
Crying, "John, John, the grey goose is gone
And the fox is on the town-o!
　　Town-o! town-o!"
Crying, "John, John, the grey goose is gone
And the fox is on the town-o!"

The fox he ran 'til he came to his den,
And there were his little ones, eight, nine, ten,
Crying, "Daddy, Daddy, better go back again,
'Cause it must be a mighty fine town-o!
    Town-o! town-o!"
Crying, "Daddy, Daddy, better go back again,
'Cause it must be a mighty fine town-o!"

Then the fox and his wife, without any strife,
Cut up the goose with a carving knife.
They never had such a supper in their life,
And the little ones chewed on the bones-o!
   Bones-o! bones-o!
They never had such a supper in their life,
And the little ones chewed on the bones-o!

The Little Duck

a Japanese poem by JŌSŌ

"I've just come from a place
    at the lake bottom!"—*that* is the look
    on the little duck's face.

The Prayer of the Little Ducks Who Went into the Ark

*a Portuguese poem
by Carmen Bernos de Gasztold*

Dear God,
Give us a flood of water.
Let it rain tomorrow and always.
Give us plenty of little slugs
and other luscious things to eat.
Protect all folk who quack
and everyone who knows how to swim.

   Amen.

 **Luscious** means delicious.

Ducks' Ditty

by Kenneth Grahame

All along the backwater,
    Through the rushes tall,
Ducks are a-dabbling,
    Up tails all!

Ducks' tails, drakes' tails,
    Yellow feet a-quiver,
Yellow bills all out of sight
    Busy in the river!

Slushy green undergrowth
    Where the roaches swim—
Here we keep our larder,
    Cool and full and dim.

Rushes means grasslike plants.
Larder means a room where food is kept.

Everyone for what he likes!
    We like to be
Heads down, tails up,
    Dabbling free!

High in the blue above
    Swifts whirl and call—
We are down a-dabbling,
    Up tails all!

The Monkeys and the Crocodile

by Laura E. Richards

Five little monkeys
  Swinging from a tree;
Teasing Uncle Crocodile,
  Merry as can be.
Swinging high, swinging low,
  Swinging left and right:
"Dear Uncle Crocodile,
  Come and take a bite!"

Five little monkeys
  Swinging in the air;
Heads up, tails up,
  Little do they care.
Swinging up, swinging down,
  Swinging far and near:
"Poor Uncle Crocodile,
  Aren't you hungry, dear?"

Four little monkeys
  Sitting in a tree;
Heads down, tails down,
  Dreary as can be.
Weeping loud, weeping low,
  Crying to each other:
"Wicked Uncle Crocodile
  To gobble up our brother!"

The Puffin

by *Robert Williams Wood*

Upon this cake of ice is perched
The paddle-footed Puffin;
To find his double we have searched,
But have discovered—Nuffin!

The Reason

by *Dorothy Aldis*

Rabbits and squirrels
Are furry and fat,
And all of the chickens
Have feathers, and *that*
Is why when it's raining
They need not stay in
The way children do who have
Only their skin.

The Owl and the Pussycat

by Edward Lear

The Owl and the Pussycat went to sea
   In a beautiful pea-green boat,
They took some honey, and plenty of money,
   Wrapped up in a five-pound note.
The Owl looked up to the stars above,
   And sang to a small guitar,
"O lovely Pussy! O Pussy, my love,
   What a beautiful Pussy you are,
         You are!
         You are!
   What a beautiful Pussy you are!"

Pussy said to the Owl, "You elegant fowl!
   How charmingly sweet you sing!
O let us be married! too long we have tarried:
   But what shall we do for a ring?"
They sailed away for a year and a day,
   To the land where the Bong-tree grows;
And there in a wood a Piggy-wig stood,
   With a ring at the end of his nose,
         His nose,
         His nose,
   With a ring at the end of his nose.

"Dear Pig, are you willing to sell for one shilling
    Your ring?" Said the Piggy, "I will."
So they took it away, and were married next day
    By the Turkey who lives on the hill.
They dined on mince, and slices of quince,
    Which they ate with a runcible spoon;
And hand in hand, on the edge of the sand,
    They danced by the light of the moon,
                The moon,
                The moon,
    They danced by the light of the moon.

Five-pound note and **shilling** are money.
Tarried means waited.
Quince means a small apple-like fruit.
Runcible spoon means a fork with three
    short, wide prongs,
    used as a spoon.

Just Play

Games with words are good to play when you are with friends or by yourself. The words are easy to remember and fun to say over and over again. Take a look at these pages full of finger rhymes, skipping rhymes, and limericks. You'll find some riddles, tongue-twisters, and haikus, too. Read them and then make up some of your own!

This Little Finger

a Costa Rican nursery rhyme

This little finger found a little egg,
This little finger cooked it,
This little finger sprinkled salt on it,
This little finger scrambled it,
And this mischievous fat one ate it!

Here Is the Family

a German nursery rhyme

This is the father, short and stout,
And this is mother, with children all about.
And this is the brother, tall you see,
And this is the sister with her dolly on her knee.
This is the baby, still to grow,
And here is the family, all in a row.

This Little Cow

a Chinese nursery rhyme

This little cow eats grass,
This little cow eats hay,
This little cow drinks water,
This little cow runs away,
And *this* little cow does nothing
But lie down all the day.

This Little Piggy

Mother Goose

This little piggy went to market,
This little piggy stayed at home,
This little piggy had roast beef,
This little piggy had none,
And this little piggy cried,
"Wee, wee, wee!"
All the way home.

135

Here Is a Bunny

author unknown

Here is a bunny
with ears so funny,

And here is her hole
in the ground.

A noise she hears.
She pricks up her ears,

And jumps into the hole
in the ground!

Itsy, Bitsy Spider

author unknown

The itsy, bitsy spider
Climbed up the water spout.
Down came the rain
And washed the spider out.
Out came the sun
And dried up all the rain.
So the itsy, bitsy spider
Climbed up the spout again.

Pat-a-Cake

Mother Goose

Pat-a-cake, pat-a-cake, baker's man,
Bake me a cake as fast as you can;
Pat it and prick it, and mark it with a B,
Put it in the oven for baby and me.

This Is the Way
the Ladies Ride

Mother Goose

This is the way the ladies ride,
Nimble-nimble, nimble-nimble,
This is the way the ladies ride,
A-nimble, nimble-nimble!

This is the way the gentlemen ride,
Gallop-a-trot, gallop-a-trot!
This is the way the gentlemen ride,
Gallop-a-gallop-a-trot!

This is the way the farmers ride,
Hobbledy-dee, hobbledy-dee,
This is the way the farmers ride,
Hobbledy-dee, hobbledy-dee,
And *down* into a ditch.

Miss Mary Mack

author unknown

Miss Mary Mack, Mack, Mack
All dressed in black, black, black
With silver buttons, buttons, buttons
All down her back, back, back
She asked her mother, mother, mother
For fifteen cents, cents, cents
To see the elephants, elephants, elephants
Climb up the fence, fence, fence
They climbed so high, high, high
They could touch the sky, sky, sky
And they never came back, back, back
'Til the fourth of July.

Ring-a-Ring o' Roses

Mother Goose

Ring-a-ring o' roses,
A pocket full of posies,
    A-tishoo! A-tishoo!
We all fall down.

Skipping Rope Rhymes

Teddy bear, teddy bear, turn around.
Teddy bear, teddy bear, touch the ground.
Teddy bear, teddy bear, tap your toe.
Teddy bear, teddy bear, out you go.

Teddy bear, teddy bear, walk upstairs.
Teddy bear, teddy bear, say your prayers.
Teddy bear, teddy bear, turn out the light.
Teddy bear, teddy bear, say good night.

Wear at the toe, skip wherever you go.
Wear at the heel, hop a great deal.
Wear at the ball, walk very tall.
Wear at the side, find a ride.
(Skipper exits.)

One to make ready,
And two to prepare;
Good luck to the rider,
And away goes the mare.

Miss, miss, little miss, miss;

When she misses, she misses like this.

(Skipper steps on rope.)

Two, four, six, eight,
Meet me at the garden gate,
If I'm late, don't wait
Two, four, six, eight . . . (until skipper misses)

Strawberry shortcake, cherry tart,
Tell me the name of my sweetheart.
A, B, C, D . . . (until skipper misses)

Apples, peaches, something sweet,
Tell me the name of your favourite treat.
A, B, C, D . . . (until skipper misses)

Down in the valley where the green grass grows,
There sat (skipper's name), sweet as a rose.
She sang, she sang, she sang so sweet!
Along came (name) and kissed her on the cheek.
How many kisses did she get?
1, 2, 3, 4, 5 . . . (until skipper misses)

Cinderella, dressed in yellow,
Went to town to kiss her fellow.
How many kisses did she get?
One, two, three . . . (until skipper misses)

I took a trip around the world,
And this is where I went:
From Arkansas to Boston;
From Boston to Canada;
From Canada to Denmark;
From Denmark to England
(and so forth, as long as the skipper can think up
new place names—or until he or she misses)

Spanish dancer, turn around,
Spanish dancer, touch the ground.
Spanish dancer, do high kicks,
Spanish dancer, do big splits.

Sally over the water,
Sally over the sea,
Sally broke a milk bottle
And blamed it on me.
Sally told Ma,
Ma told Pa,
Sally got a scolding,
Ha, ha, ha.

"Mother, Mother, I am ill.
Call the doctor over the hill."
In came the doctor.
In came the nurse.
In came the lady with the alligator purse.
"Measles," said the doctor.
"Mumps," said the nurse.
"Nothing," said the lady with the alligator purse.

Tongue Twisters

Try to say each of the following twisters fast, without getting your tongue twisted. Which ones can you say fast three times in a row?

A big baby buggy with rubber buggy bumpers

✖

Toy boat, toy boat, toy boat

✖

Black bug's blood, black bug's blood

✖

Does your shirt shop stock short socks with spots?

✖

Double bubble gum doubles bubbles.

✖

Find fresh fried fish free at the fish fry.

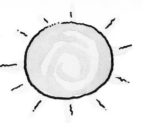

Round and round the rugged rock the ragged rascal ran.

✖

A cat ran over the roof with a lump of raw liver.

✖

A pale pink proud peacock pompously preened its pretty plumage.

✖

Swan, swim over the sea.
Swim, swan, swim!
Swan, swim back again.
Well swum, swan!

✖

My dame hath a lame tame crane.
My dame hath a crane that is lame.
Pray, gentle Jane, let my dame's tame crane
Feed and come home again.

✖

The sixth sheik's sixth sheep's sick.

✖

Sheep shouldn't sleep in a shack.
Sheep should sleep in a shed.

✖

Some shun sunshine.

Betty Botter bought some butter,
"But," she said, "this butter's bitter.
If I put it in my batter,
It will make my batter bitter.
But a bit of better butter
That would make my batter better."
So she bought a bit of better butter
Better than her bitter butter,
And she put it in her batter.
Then her batter was not bitter.
So 'twas better Betty Botter
Bought a bit of better butter.

People say Peter Piper picked a peck of pickled peppers.
A peck of pickled peppers Peter Piper picked.
But if Peter Piper really picked a peck of pickled peppers,
Where is the peck of pickled peppers Peter Piper picked?

How much wood would a woodchuck chuck
If a woodchuck could chuck wood?
A woodchuck would chuck all the wood in a truck
If a woodchuck could chuck wood.

She sells seashells on the seashore.
The shells she sells shine I am sure.
She sells shiny sea shells on the seashore.

Stan's store stocked stunning sturdy ships.
The ships were shipshape for shipping
and for sailing the shallow shores.

Three grey geese in a green field grazing,
Grey were the geese, and green was the grazing.

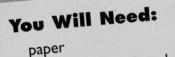

Make Your Own Tongue Twisters

Do you enjoy tongue-tangling words? If you do, you can try making up tongue twisters of your own.

Tongue twisters work because they make you repeat the same sounds—or sounds that are almost alike—so many times that your tongue trips! Below are some steps you can follow to build a tongue twister.

You Will Need:

paper
a pencil or felt-tipped
pen

What To Do:

1. Make up phrases (groups of words) or sentences in which all or most of the words begin with the same sound. For example:

a big bat

2. Think of other words that have almost the same beginning sound. Add those words to the phrase or sentence. For example, some words begin with **bl** or **br**. You can add words to make sentences like these:

Brown bats eat black bugs.
Bats eat bugs, but the bugs bite back.

3. Try out your sentence by saying it rapidly five times. Does it twist your tongue? You can try adding more words or changing some words to make it harder to say. For example, you might try this:

Do brown bats eat black bugs, brown bugs, or blue bugs?
Brown bats bite bugs, but the bugs bite the brown bats back.

4. When you have a sentence that really tangles your tongue, try out your tongue twister with friends. You and your friends can make up other tongue twisters to say.

Jabberwocky

by Lewis Carroll

'Twas Brillig, and the slithy toves
    Did gyre and gimble in the wabe:
All mimsy were the borogoves,
    And the mome raths outgrabe.

"Beware the Jabberwock, my son!
    The jaws that bite, the claws that catch!
Beware the Jubjub bird, and shun
    The frumious Bandersnatch!"

He took his vorpal sword in hand:
    Long time the manxome foe he sought—
So rested he by the Tumtum tree,
    And stood awhile in thought.

And, as in uffish thought he stood,
    The Jabberwock, with eyes of flame,
Came whiffling through the tulgey wood,
    And burbled as it came!

One, two! One, two! And through and through
    The vorpal blade went snicker-snack!
He left it dead, and with its head
    He went galumphing back.

"And hast thou slain the Jabberwock?
    Come to my arms, my beamish boy!
O frabjous day! Callooh! Callay!"
    He chortled in his joy.

'Twas brillig, and the slithy toves
    Did gyre and gimble in the wabe:
All mimsy were the borogoves,
    And the mome raths outgrabe.

This is a famous and fun nonsense poem.
Did you read it without tangling your tongue?

World Riddles

Riddles are probably the oldest of all games. In ancient times, people who could make up and solve riddles were thought to be the best leaders and the wisest. Riddles were used to teach children many important facts of life. Almost everybody in the world plays the riddle game. Try to solve these. Then check your answers against those on page 155.

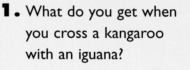

1. What do you get when you cross a kangaroo with an iguana?

2. Why do leopards have a hard time hiding?

3. Where do you find oceans without water, forests without trees, motorways without cars, and cities without people?

4. How many times can you subtract 9 from 99?

Rhymes and Riddles

Riddles are like puzzles or tricks with words. The answers
are surprising. Can you solve these riddles? Some of them
rhyme. Look at the pictures for clues.

1. Riddle me, riddle me, what is that,
   Over the head and under the hat?

2. Runs all day and never walks,
   Often murmurs, never talks;
   It has a bed and never sleeps;
   It has a mouth and never eats.

3. A riddle, a riddle, as I suppose,
   a hundred eyes and never a nose.

4. A house full, a hole full,
   And you cannot gather a bowl full.

5. Never seen,
   Only heard,
   I only speak when spoken to.

6. I appear once in a minute,
   Once in a blue moon,
   Yet never in one hundred years.

7. I disguise myself to confuse you,
   But once you know me,
   I can never fool you.

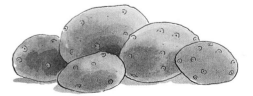

Answers:

1. hair
2. a river
3. a potato
4. smoke or mist
5. an echo
6. the letter m
7. a riddle

Limericks

A limerick is a clever and funny form of verse. It consists of five short lines. The first two lines always rhyme with the fifth line. No one knows who invented the form, but it takes its name from the city of Limerick in Ireland.

There was a Young Lady of Crete,
Who was so exceedingly neat,
When she got out of bed
She stood on her head,
To make sure of not soiling her feet.

author unknown

There was a Young Maid who asked, "Why
Can't I look in my ear with my eye?
If I give my mind to it,
I'm sure I can do it,
You never can tell till you try."

by Edward Lear

There was a Young Lady of Niger
Who smiled as she rode on a tiger.
They came back from the ride
With the lady inside
And the smile on the face of the tiger.

author unknown

There was a Young Lady of Lynn,
Who was so uncommonly thin
 That when she essayed
 To drink lemonade,
She slipped through the straw and fell in.

   author unknown

Essayed means tried.

A fly and a flea in a flue
Were imprisoned, so what could they do?
 Said the fly, "Let us flee!"
 "Let us fly!" said the flea.
So they flew through a flaw in the flue.

   author unknown

An epicure dining at Crewe
Once found a large mouse in his stew.
 Said the waiter, "Don't shout
 And wave it about,
Or the rest will be wanting one too!"

   author unknown

Epicure means a person who
 enjoys eating and drinking.

A cheerful Old Bear at the Zoo
Could always find something to do.
   When it bored him to go
   On a walk to and fro
He reversed it, and walked fro and to.

author unknown

There was an Old Man with a beard,
Who said, "It is just as I feared!
   Two Owls and a Hen,
   Four Larks and a Wren
Have built their nests in my beard."

by Edward Lear

There was an Old Man from Peru
Who dreamed he was eating his shoe.
   He woke in a fright.
   In the middle of the night
And found it was perfectly true.

author unknown

There was an Old Man who said, "Do
Tell me how I should add two and two?
    I think more and more
    That it makes about four—
But I fear that is almost too few."

author unknown

There was a Young Woman named Bright,
Whose speed was much faster than light.
    She set out one day
    In a relative way,
And returned on the previous night.

author unknown

There was an Old Person of Ware,
Who rode on the back of a bear.
    When they asked, "Does it trot?"
    He said, "Certainly *not*!
It's a Moppsikon Floppsikon bear!"

by Edward Lear

The bottle of perfume that Willie sent
Was highly displeasing to Millicent.
    Her thanks were so cold
    That they quarrelled, I'm told,
Through that silly scent Willie sent Millicent.

author unknown

Write a Poem with Rhythm and Rhyme

TRY THIS!
1

Can you write a poem? Of course you can. If you ever make up songs or silly sayings with rhyming words, you are already making up poems. You can use rhythms and rhymes to create beautiful poems or funny poems or just plain silly poems. Here are some ways to start.

What To Do:

You Will Need:
paper
a pencil or felt-tipped
pen

1. Many poems have a regular beat, or
rhythm, just like skipping or dancing.
They may have many strong beats or
only a few. Say these lines aloud. They
have four strong beats.

> There **was** an old **wom**an who **lived** in a **shoe**.
> (soft, **strong**)

> **Hump**ty **Dump**ty **had** a great **fall**.
> (**strong,** soft)

These lines have three strong beats:
> **Ring**-a-**ring** o' **ros**es,
> A **pock**et **full** of **pos**ies,

Make up two or more lines of your own with
the same rhythm.

2. Many poems have rhymes. Rhyming words have
the same ending sounds and different beginning
sounds. Listen for rhyming words in these lines:

> One, **two,**
> Buckle my **shoe;**
> Three, **four,**
> Knock at the **door;**

Make up two or more lines with the same
ending sounds. You can have each group of two
lines rhyme or have every other line rhyme.
Next, make more poems and longer ones using
your favourite rhythms and rhymes.

Haikus

A haiku is a Japanese form of poetry that does not rhyme. Many haikus are about something in nature and suggest a season or time of year. Read these haikus, then try writing your own.

A mountain village
deep in snow . . . under the drifts
a sound of water

by Shiki

When my canary
Flew away, that was the end
Of spring in my house.

by Shiki

In spring the chirping
Frogs sing like birds . . . in summer
They bark like old dogs.

by Onitsura

What a wonderful
day! No one in the village
    doing anything.

    by Shiki

Get out of my road
And allow me to plant these
    Bamboos, Mr. Toad!

    by Chora

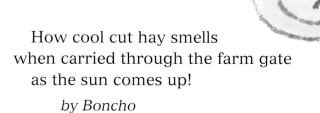

  How cool cut hay smells
when carried through the farm gate
    as the sun comes up!

    by Boncho

How to Create Syllable Poems

Different kinds of poems have different syllable patterns. Haikus have three lines that do not rhyme. The first line has five syllables, the second line has seven, and the third line has five. Its syllable pattern is five, seven, five. Another kind of syllable poem is the cinquain. A cinquain has five lines that do not rhyme. Its syllable pattern is two, four, six, eight, two.

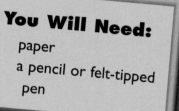

You Will Need:

paper

a pencil or felt-tipped pen

What To Do:

1. Try making a haiku or a cinquain of your own. Describe how something looks, feels, sounds, smells, or tastes. Remember to count your syllables.

This haiku suggests summer:

> How cool cut hay smells
> *(5 syllables)*
> When carried through the farm gate
> *(7 syllables)*
> As the sun comes up.
> *(5 syllables)*

Here is a cinquain:

> Rainy
> *(2 syllables)*
> Windy morning—
> *(4 syllables)*
> Lights on in the kitchen,
> *(6 syllables)*
> Warm, toasty smells. "You're late," Mum yells.
> *(8 syllables)*
> "Coming!"
> *(2 syllables)*

2. Make up your own kind of syllable poem and write a poem in that form.

3. Make a diary of syllable poems. Whenever you notice something interesting that you want to remember, write a syllable poem about it. Soon you'll have your own collection of poems to enjoy.

Wise Words

Fables are old stories that teach a lesson, or moral. They usually have animals as the main characters. Proverbs are old sayings that give good advice. The moral of a fable or the advice in a proverb may sound puzzling the first time you hear it. But when you think carefully about the words, the lesson taught can become clearer.

The Lion and the Mouse

by Aesop

Once, when a lion was asleep, a little mouse
began running up and down upon him.
This soon wakened the lion. Angry at being
disturbed, the lion placed his huge paw upon
the little mouse and opened his big jaws to
swallow him.

"Pardon, O King," cried the little mouse.
"If you will let me go, I shall never forget your
kindness. Who knows—I may be able to do
you a good turn one day."

The lion was so amused at the idea of the
mouse being able to help him that he lifted up
his paw and let him go.

Some time later, the little mouse heard the
lion roaring angrily. When he went to see what
the trouble was, he found the lion caught in a
hunter's net. Remembering his promise, the
little mouse set to work nibbling at the ropes
with his sharp teeth. And before long, the lion
was able to crawl out of the net.

The moral of this story is that little friends
may prove to be great friends.

The Crow and the Jug

by Aesop

A crow, half-dead with thirst, came upon a jug that had once been full of water. But when the crow put his beak into the jug, he found that there was only a little water left in it. Try as he would, he could not reach far enough down to get a drink.

Then a thought came to him. He took a pebble and dropped it into the jug. Then he took another pebble, and another, and dropped them into the jug. Before long, he could see the water rising higher and higher. After dropping in a few more pebbles he was able to get a drink.

The moral of this story is that little by little does the trick.

The Hare and the Tortoise

by Aesop

The hare was once boasting of his speed to the other animals. "I have never yet been beaten," said he. "I can run faster than any of you. I challenge anyone here to race with me."

The tortoise said quietly, "I accept your challenge."

"That is a good joke," the hare laughed. "I could dance around you all the way."

"Keep your boasting until you've won," answered the tortoise. "Shall we race?"

So a course was fixed and a start was made. The hare darted out of sight at once. Soon, knowing that he was far ahead, he stopped to have a nap.

Meanwhile the tortoise plodded along, slowly and steadily. When the hare awoke from his nap, he saw the tortoise nearing the finish line. The hare leapt up and ran as fast as he could. But he was too late. The tortoise won the race.

The moral of this story is that slow and steady wins the race.

The Ant and the Dove

by Aesop

An Ant was speeding along on its three pairs of
legs when suddenly, it stopped.

"I'm thirsty," the Ant said aloud.

"Why don't you get a drink of water from the brook?"
cooed a Dove perched in a nearby tree. "The brook
is close by. Just be careful you don't fall in."

The Ant sped to the brook and began to drink. But
a sudden gust of wind blew the Ant into the water.

"Help!" cried the Ant, "I'm drowning!"

The Dove knew it had to act quickly to save the Ant.
With its beak, the Dove broke a twig from the tree.
Then the Dove flew over the brook and dropped the
twig to the Ant. The Ant climbed onto the twig and
floated safely ashore.

Not long afterwards, the Ant saw a Hunter. He was
setting a trap to catch the Dove. The Dove began to
fly towards the trap.

The Ant knew it had to act quickly to save the Dove.
So the Ant opened its strong jaws and bit the bare
ankle of the Hunter.

"Ouch!" the Hunter cried.

The Dove heard the Hunter and flew away to safety.

*The moral of this story is that one good turn
deserves another.*

The Dog and the Bone

by Aesop

It so happened that a dog had a fine bone and was carrying it home to chew on in peace. On his way, he had to cross a plank set over a stream.

As he walked across the plank, he looked down and saw his reflection in the water. Thinking that it was another dog with another bone, he made up his mind to have that bone too. But when he snapped at his reflection, his own bone fell into the water and was lost forever.

The moral of this story is that the greedy often lose what they have.

How Chameleon Became a Teacher

a story from Benin, Africa, translated and retold by Raouf Mama

Once upon a time, Crocodile and Chameleon were friends. Crocodile was very fond of sunbathing. Nothing gave him greater pleasure than to come splashing out of the water and to lie on the sand in bright sunshine. And whenever Crocodile came out of the water, Chameleon would come out of the bush and climb up a tree nearby. Soon, they would be heard chattering merrily and sending peals of laughter soaring through the air as though they had not a care in the world. Occasionally, they would be seen lying a short distance from each other, whispering, shaking their heads, or nodding as though the fate of the whole world hung upon the outcome of their consultations. Crocodile and Chameleon seemed to be very good friends.

Peals means loud, long sounds.
Consultations means discussions.

One day, as they were about to go their separate ways, Crocodile invited Chameleon to dinner. "Come to my house, at the bottom of the lake," he said. "My whole family would love to meet you and have you over for dinner. Jump right into the lake when you see me rise to the surface, and I will take you to my house." They agreed on a day and a time, Chameleon thanked Crocodile for his kindness, and they took leave of each other.

On the appointed day, Chameleon went to the shore of the lake, carrying a stick. While Chameleon waited, Crocodile gathered his wife and children together in their living room at the bottom of the lake and told them, "Rejoice! Rejoice! Chameleon, whom I have befriended, is coming to see us! He will be our special treat! I cannot tell you what a delicacy he will make! Chameleon meat is so tasty," he concluded, smacking his jaws and rolling his eyes.

> **Befriended** means made friends with.
> **Delicacy** means a very good or choice food.

179

So speaking, Crocodile went out to meet his friend. There was a great disturbance on the face of the lake as he came splashing into view close to the shore, his gigantic jaws wide apart. As though to test his friend, Chameleon threw his stick into the water. Believing that Chameleon himself had dived into the lake, Crocodile lunged forward and, with a blood-chilling crunch, closed his enormous jaws over the stick.

Trembling in terror, his heart racing furiously, Chameleon fled from the shore and scrambled up the closest tree. Then, taking cover and blending in with the foliage, he cried, "What would have become of me if I hadn't thrown my stick into the lake to test my friend! Thank goodness I didn't step in to meet Crocodile as he had instructed me,

Foliage means the leaves of a plant.

for I would have ended up in the bottom of his stomach instead of as a guest at his house. Take note! Take note, O world! Caution is the mother of safety!"

And so it was that Chameleon became a teacher of prudence and wisdom. Except when in danger, he treads ever so carefully, thinks long and hard before putting a foot forward, and takes on the local colour wherever he happens to be.

This tale warns people against putting their trust in a "friend" without first giving him or her a test.

Caution means being careful.
Prudence means thinking before acting.
Treads means walks.

World Proverbs

Most proverbs are so old that no one knows when they were first said. Some proverbs suggest the best way to do something. Others tell how to get along with people. And some tell people how they should behave. Proverbs are often much the same from one land to another. Many give the same advice in slightly different ways.

England: Haste makes waste.

China: Mistakes happen because of haste, never by doing a thing slowly.

Spain: Who pours water into a bottle with haste, spills more than he gets in.

Puerto Rico: See before you tie how you can untie.

These proverbs mean that if you try to do something too quickly, you will not do it well.

Spain: What cures Sancho makes Martha sick.

England: One man's meat is another man's poison.

France: What is bad for one person is good for another.

These proverbs mean that people like different things. You may like something very much, but others may not like it.

Italy: Hunger is the best cook.

India: Hunger has no taste.

France: To a hungry man, there is no bad bread.

These proverbs mean that if you are hungry enough, you'll enjoy anything. You won't care what it tastes like.

Index by Author

If you know the name of the poet or author you are looking for, use this index. You can also find a poem or rhyme by using the **Index by Title** starting on page 185, the **Index by First Line** starting on page 188, or the **Index by Subject** starting on page 189. For poems or rhymes in all other volumes, see the entry **poems and rhymes** in the **General Index** in Volume 15.

Index by Title

If you know the title of the poem or rhyme you are looking for, use this index. You can also find a poem or rhyme by using the **Index by Author** starting on page 184, the **Index by First Line** starting on page 188, or the **Index by Subject** starting on page 189. For poems or rhymes in all other volumes, see the entry **poems and rhymes** in the **General Index** in Volume 15.

187

Index by First Line

Use this index to find a poem or rhyme if you know its first line. You can also find a poem or rhyme by using the **Index by Author** starting on page 184, the **Index by Title** starting on page 185, or the **Index by Subject** starting on page 189. For poems and rhymes in all other volumes, see the entry **poems and rhymes** in the **General Index** in Volume 15.

Index by Subject

Use this index to find a poem or rhyme about a particular subject. You can also find a poem or rhyme by using the **Index by Author** starting on page 184, the **Index by Title** starting on page 185, or the **Index by First Line** starting on page 188. For poems or rhymes in all other volumes, see the entry **poems and rhymes** in the **General Index** in Volume 15.

Illustration Acknowledgments

The Publishers of *Childcraft* gratefully acknowledge the courtesy of the following illustrators, photographers, agencies, and organizations for illustrations in this volume. When all the illustrations for a sequence of pages are from a single source, the inclusive page numbers are given. Credits should be read from top to bottom, left to right, on their respective pages. All illustrations are the exclusive property of the publishers of *Childcraft* unless names are marked with an asterisk(*).

Cover	*Hey Diddle Diddlle*—William McBride with Pat Moss and Michael Stack (Photograph © Robb Gregg Studios); Knave of Hearts—Linda Gist; Moon—Kathy Ember; Frog—Tanya Roitman
Back Cover	Linda Gist
1	Kathy Ember; Linda Gist; Tanya Roitman
4-5	Tanya Roitman; Kinuko Craft; Dennis Hockerman
6-7	Diane Paterson; Steven D. Mach
8-9	Joan Holub; Yoshi Miyake
12-13	Linda Gist; Lisa Cinelli; Kinuko Craft; Uri Shulevitz
14-15	Kinuko Craft; Blanche L. Sims
16-17	Jan Brett
18-19	Linda Liefer
20-21	Linda Gist
22-23	Lucinda McQueen; Kinuko Craft
24-25	Betsy Day; Kinuko Craft
26-27	Susan Lexa
28-29	Kinuko Craft; Uri Shulevitz
30-31	Kinuko Craft; Linda Liefer
32-33	Ron LeHew; Nan Brooks; Blanche L. Sims
34-35	Kinuko Craft
36-37	Ron LeHew; Blanche L. Sims
38-39	Dennis Hockerman
40-41	Lucinda McQueen
42-43	Christine Willis
44-45	Mou-sien Tseng; Yoshi Miyake
46-47	Yoshi Miyake; Kinuko Craft
48-49	Jan Brett; Laura D'Argo
50-51	Lisa Cinelli; Kathy Ember; Dennis Hockerman
52-53	Diane Paterson; Nan Brooks; Dennis Hockerman; Joan Holub
54-63	Diane Paterson
64-66	Nan Brooks
67-68	E. H. Shepard*; Dennis Hockerman
69-73	Dennis Hockerman
74-75	Nan Brooks
76-77	Diane Paterson; Joan Holub
78-79	Steven D. Mach
80-81	Diane Paterson
82-83	Nan Brooks; Dennis Hockerman
84-85	Mou-sien Tseng; Robert Byrd
86-87	Mou-sien Tseng
88-89	Dennis Hockerman; Marlene Ekman
90-91	Dick Keller*
92-93	Tanya Roitman; Gerardo Suzan; Blanche L. Sims; Yoshi Miyake
94-95	Jan Brett; Yoshi Miyake
96-97	Ron LeHew
98-99	Kinuko Craft
100-101	Blanche L. Sims; Eileen Mueller Neill
102-103	Blanche L. Sims
104-105	Ron LeHew; Kinuko Craft
106-107	Susan Lexa
108-109	Robert Byrd; Yoshi Miyake
110-111	Tanya Roitman
112-113	Ron LeHew; Blanche L. Sims
114-115	Garth Williams
116-117	Drew-Brook-Cormack Associates; Gerardo Suzan
118-119	Susan Lexa
120-125	Linda Liefer
126-127	Pat & Robin Dewitt; Pamela Ford Johnson
128-129	Robert Byrd
130-131	Ron LeHew
132-133	Carl Whiting; Freddie Levin; Dick Martin
134-135	Jan Brett; John Nez
136-137	Michael Chesworth; Jan Brett
138-139	Linda Liefer
140-145	Freddie Levin
146-151	Carl Whiting
152-153	Carolyn Croll; John Tenniel*
154-155	Dick Martin
156-157	Malcolm Livingstone; John Nez; Dick Martin
158-159	David Mostyn
160-161	David Mostyn; Lisa Cinelli
162-163	Steven D. Mach
164-165	Koko Fukazawa; WORLD BOOK illustration
166-167	Sarah Figlio
168-169	Lisa Cinelli; Jack Lefkowitz; Tanya Roitman; Yoshi Miyake
170-171	Yoshi Miyake
172-173	Jane Kochnewitz
174-175	Robert Byrd
176-181	Tanya Roitman
182-183	Jack Lefkowitz